D0539733

What are panic attacks?

Panic attacks are extremely frightening. They seem to come out of the blue, strike at random, make people feel powerless, out of control, and as if they are about to die or go mad. Many people experience this problem, but many also learn to cope and, eventually, to overcome it successfully.

A panic attack is an exaggeration of the body's normal response to fear, stress or excitement. When faced with a situation seen as potentially threatening, the body automatically gears itself up for danger, by producing quantities of adrenalin for 'fight or flight'. This would have prepared our cave-dwelling ancestors to fight or run away from danger, but it's much less appropriate to the stresses we encounter today.

Adrenalin has the following effects on your body:
• The muscles tense up.
• Breathing becomes faster to take in more oxygen, which muscles need to help them transform sugar into energy.
• The heart pumps harder to get blood to where it's needed.
• Blood is diverted to the muscles, away from areas that don't need it, so you become pale.
• Digestion slows down and salivary glands dry up, causing a dry mouth.
• Your senses become more alert; the slightest sound or touch provokes a reaction.
• Sweating increases.

These reactions occur in a matter of seconds, and can happen in moments of pleasurable excitement, as well as in fear-provoking and threatening situations.

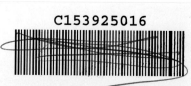

C153925016

How to...
cope with panic attacks

When adrenalin floods your body, it can cause a number of different physical and emotional sensations that may affect you during a panic attack.

These may include:
- very rapid breathing or feeling unable to breathe
- very rapid heartbeat
- pains in your chest
- feeling faint or dizzy
- sweating
- ringing in your ears
- tingling or numbness in your hands and feet
- hot or cold flushes
- feeling nauseous
- wanting to go to the toilet
- feelings of absolute terror
- feelings of unreality, called depersonalisation and derealisation.

(During depersonalisation, people feel detached from their body and surroundings, strange and unreal. During derealisation, they feel grounded in themselves, but the world seems distant or strange, and they may feel unsteady on their feet.)

Panic attacks come on very quickly, symptoms usually peaking within 10 minutes. Most panic attacks last for between five and 20 minutes. Some people report attacks lasting for up to an hour, but they are likely to be experiencing one attack after another, or a high level of anxiety after the initial attack. You may have one or two panic attacks and never experience another. Or you may have attacks once a month or several times each week.

Panic attacks can come in the night when you are asleep. These night-time attacks occur as your body is on 'high alert' and can detect small, normal changes in your body which it then takes as a sign of danger. (The fact that you can be monitoring your bodily sensations while asleep is perfectly normal and automatic – just think about the times you have woken up and needed to go to the toilet.) Night-time attack may be particularly frightening, as you may feel confused and helpless to do anything to spot it coming.

This is one of the most distressing aspects of suffering from panic attacks – they may seem completely unpredictable, and therefore uncontrollable.

During an attack, you may fear that the world is going to come to an end, or that you are about to die or go mad. The most important thing to remember is that, however dreadful you may feel during an attack, this is not going to happen. The bodily effects of panic attacks, such as breathlessness, are just part of the panic. If you would like further reassurance, see your GP, so he or she can rule out any physical cause for your symptoms.

How do panic attacks become a problem?

A high level of adrenalin is not in itself a bad thing. It can give you the extra energy to deal with difficult demands and challenges. The damage is done when the levels of adrenalin don't fall, naturally, after a stressful event. Stress becomes prolonged and tension becomes a habit.

For many people, their first panic attack comes out of the blue and creates a state of arousal. You may find yourself becoming more nervous, impatient and irritable as you feel, understandably, apprehensive about having another attack.

5

How to...
cope with panic attacks

If you experience panic attacks over a period of time, you may develop a fear of fear. Because you have become hyper-aware of the sensations associated with fear – sensitised to them – you tense up whenever anything at all reminds you of the original panic. This can include your own bodily sensations. So someone feeling hot, or with sweaty hands (perhaps because they are in a meeting in a warm room), may assume, automatically, that they are in for another panic attack. Anticipating this makes them tense up and produces the very panic response they feared.

Agoraphobia and similar problems
You may start to associate particular places and situations with having an attack. In an attempt to avoid another one, you may steer clear of places where attacks have previously occurred. But this may put more and more restrictions on your day-to-day activities, and could lead to agoraphobia or social phobia. (See Mind's booklet *Understanding phobias,* details under *Further reading,* on p. 15.)

Depression
As you feel more out of control and restrict your activities, your enjoyment of life and your self-confidence is undermined. Many people who experience panic attacks become very depressed.

What causes these attacks?

There are many physical and psychological factors, which may be interwoven. You may experience panic only in response to a particular situation, such as flying or visiting the dentist. Or you may feel perfectly fine during a stressful event, but may have an attack later. This is because adrenalin levels don't drop straight away. Any major life changes and events can trigger panic attacks.

Childhood influences
Incidents in childhood, and the way you were brought up and taught to think about yourself, can make you vulnerable to panic attacks later on. If you experienced great fear at being separated from a parent, you may have gone on to develop school phobia. As an adult, you may then have panic attacks when threatened with the loss of a support system or of someone who is important to you. Adult survivors of abuse in childhood also frequently suffer panic attacks.

Personality traits
If you are always anxious, you are more likely to have panic attacks. Being over-critical and disapproving of yourself, and striving to conform to the expectations of others, is common in people who panic. You may have difficulties in expressing your own needs and asserting yourself.

Physical causes
There are a number of physical causes that could be causing or contributing to your panic attacks:
- Unstable blood sugar levels (hypoglycaemia) can be the result of poor eating habits, dieting and fasting.
- Over-breathing (hyperventilation) happens when you are under stress, though you may not be aware of it. Your breathing becomes more rapid, in order to meet the body's demand for more oxygen for the muscles. As a result, you breathe out more carbon-dioxide than normal, which can bring on panic symptoms.
- Digestive problems, particularly food allergies, may be to blame.
- Taking antidepressants, particularly the newer ones, may produce panic attacks, especially at first.
- Caffeine, cigarettes, alcohol, and certain street drugs (such as LSD, marijuana and cocaine) can bring on a panic reaction.
- Withdrawing from any drug that has a sedative effect, such as nicotine, alcohol and tranquillisers, can do the same.

7

- Some prescription medication, including some amphetamines, steroids, anti-asthma drugs, and even nasal decongestants have been reported to increase anxiety.
- Sometimes, problems with the way the brain works (known as organic brain dysfunction) will cause balance, coordination and visual difficulties that make people very vulnerable to stress, and may contribute to agoraphobia.
- Being in chronic pain can be another cause of panic attacks, as can simple jet lag.

How can I help myself?

Your panic attacks are likely to make you feel out of control and dependent; the victim of your bodily reactions and outside circumstances. The first step along the road to recovery is recognising that you have the power to control your symptoms.

Take control
Start by really looking, in detail, at your panic attacks. When did they happen? Where were you? What were you thinking? See if you can identify particular thoughts that trigger a panic reaction.

A number of experts have emphasised the need to accept the panic attacks when they occur and that it may in fact be most helpful if you try and ride out the attacks to learn that no harm will come to you. This may sound strange, but fighting them only increases your level of fear and allows your panic to take on tremendous proportions. Accept that a panic attack is unpleasant and embarrassing, but that it isn't life-threatening or the end of the world. By going with the panic, you are reducing its power to terrify you.

Creative visualisation and affirmations

Creative visualisation and affirmations are techniques that may be helpful. You can use them to re-train your imagination and to get yourself moving in a more positive direction.

Many people who suffer panic attacks have a vivid imagination, which they use to conjure up disaster, illness and death. You can train your imagination to focus on situations that give you a sense of wellbeing. You can imagine you are in a place that symbolises peace and relaxation for you, such as drifting on a lake. You can practise this anywhere but, until you have got used to doing this, try sitting in a chair with your limbs as floppy as possible, and think of calming images.

You can use visualisation to focus on situations that you fear. Imagine the situation and speak positively to yourself: 'I am doing well', 'This is easy'. These simple, positive, present-tense affirmations are messages that you can say silently or out loud.

These techniques do not provide a quick fix. If you have been used to thinking negatively, over a long period of time, you will need to practise every day. You may then gradually notice positive changes in the way you think of yourself and others.

Assertiveness

You may be having panic attacks because there are aspects of your life that are undermining your confidence. It may be useful to look at your family life, your job, and so on, and identify changes you would like to make. If you feel trapped in a situation, and find it very difficult to express your true feelings (to say 'no' or to set proper limits in relationships, for example), you may find assertiveness training helpful.

How to...
cope with panic attacks

Learn a relaxation technique

If you habitually clench your jaw, and your shoulders are tensed up, this will generate further stress. Relaxation techniques focus on easing muscle tension and slowing down your breathing. It helps your mind to relax. (See *The Mind guide to relaxation*.)

Breathing

Hyperventilation (over-breathing) commonly leads to panic attacks. Many people get into the habit of breathing shallowly, from the upper chest, rather than more slowly from the abdomen. Put one hand on your upper chest and the other on your stomach. Notice which hand moves as you breathe. The hand on your chest should hardly move, if you are breathing correctly from the diaphragm, but the hand on your stomach should rise and fall. Practise this breathing, slowly and calmly, every day.

Diet

Unstable blood sugar levels can contribute to symptoms of panic. Eat regularly and avoid sugary foods and drinks, white flour and junk food. Instead, choose complex carbohydrates, such as potatoes, rice and pasta. Caffeine, alcohol and smoking all contribute to panic attacks and are best avoided.

First aid

If you are having a panic attack, try cupping your hands over your nose and mouth, or holding a paper bag (not plastic!) and breathing into it, for about 10 minutes. This should raise the level of carbon-dioxide in the bloodstream and relieve symptoms.

Other first-aid tips include running on the spot during a panic attack. If you feel unreal, carry an object, such as the photograph of a loved one, to maintain a sense of reality, or touch a heavily textured object, such as a strip of sandpaper. You could also distract yourself, by trying to focus on what is going on around you.

Which therapies are effective?

Drug therapy
The NICE (National Institute of Health and Clinical Excellence) guidelines on the treatment of anxiety state that benzodiazepine tranquillisers, such as diazepam (Valium), are associated with a less good outcome in the long-term and should not be used to treat panic disorder. If drug treatment is used, an SSRI antidepressant licensed for panic disorder, such as citalopram (Cipramil), should be used first, and if this is not effective, the tricyclic antidepressants imipramine or clomipramine (Anafranil) may be tried instead. Antidepressants, especially SSRIs, are difficult to come off for many people, so when you are ready to stop taking them, you should always withdraw slowly.

When starting antidepressants, the side effects may include anxious, jittery feelings. The longer you are on them, the more likely you are to experience withdrawal symptoms, which can include panic attacks. (See Mind's *Making sense of* series, details under *Further reading*, on p. 15.)

How to...
cope with panic attacks

Psychotherapy

Emotional conflicts and past difficulties may lead to anxiety, which is released through panic attacks. Without realising it, you may be experiencing these bodily sensations and physical reactions as a way of avoiding painful emotions. Psychotherapy can help you to understand how your present reactions are affected by past difficulties, and to overcome them. (For more information, see *Useful organisations,* on p. 14.)

Cognitive behaviour therapy (CBT)

Our thoughts have a very powerful impact on our behaviour. You may be unaware of seemingly automatic thoughts and misinterpretations that provoke attacks. This is because thoughts happen so quickly and may take the form of images and sensations, rather than words.

The way we interpret things can cause extreme distress. But it is possible to bring about a state of wellbeing by changing habitual thought patterns. If we think that our racing heart is a sign of a possible heart attack we'll be very frightened, but if we think that it is due to excitement or too much coffee, we'll feel very differently about it.

CBT aims to identify and change the negative thought patterns and misinterpretations that can feed panic attacks. If you are interested in this kind of therapy, ask your GP to refer you to a clinical psychologist. It's also possible to apply self-help techniques. (See *Making sense of cognitive behaviour therapy,* details under *Further reading,* on p. 15.)

Behaviour therapy

Many people develop a pattern of avoiding situations that have previously provoked a panic attack. They may become withdrawn and phobic. A clinical psychologist can address the problem using behavioural therapy. The therapy concentrates on encouraging you to imagine anxiety-provoking situations, at the same time as practising relaxation. You will be encouraged to confront your fears, in fantasy, and then move on to facing your fears in reality. In learning to relax and face up to feared situations, you will unlearn your feelings of panic.

Complementary and alternative therapies

Complementary and alternative therapies can be helpful when people are experiencing stress-related symptoms, anxiety and depression. They can be a useful tool in promoting relaxation and inducing a state of wellbeing.

Complementary health practitioners stress the connections between mind and body, and aren't concerned with merely treating symptoms. There is an enormous number of different therapies: acupuncture, aromatherapy, autogenic training and homeopathy, to name but a few. (See *Useful organisations*, on p. 14, and *Further reading,* on p. 15, for more information.)

Useful organisations

Mind
Mind is the leading mental health organisation in England and Wales, providing a unique range of services through its local associations, to enable people with experience of mental distress to have a better quality of life. For more information about any mental health issues, including details of your nearest local Mind association, contact the Mind website: www.mind.org.uk or Mind*info*Line on 0845 766 0163.

British Association for Behavioural Cognitive Psychotherapies (BABCP)
tel: 0161 797 4484, web: www.babcp.com
Promote CBT and provides a list of private accredited therapists

British Association for Counselling and Psychotherapy (BACP)
BACP House, 35–37 Albert Street, Rugby CV21 2SG
tel: 01455 883 300 (general enquiries)
tel: 0870 443 5220 (to find a therapist)
web: www.bacp.co.uk
See website or phone for details of local practitioners

The Institute for Complementary Medicine (ICM)
tel: 020 7922 7980, web: www.i-c-m.org.uk
Has a register of professional, competent practitioners

Anxiety UK (formerly the National Phobics Society)
tel: 0870 775 774, web: www.anxietyuk.org.uk
For those suffering from anxiety disorders

No Panic
helpline: 0808 808 0545, web: www.nopanic.org.uk
Helps people experiencing panic and anxiety disorders